The Lost Sheep

Written by Bethan Lycett

Illustrated by Hannah Stout

10

This is a story that Jesus told
of a little sheep who went out from the fold.
The gate was left open wide one day,
and into the lane little sheep went to play.

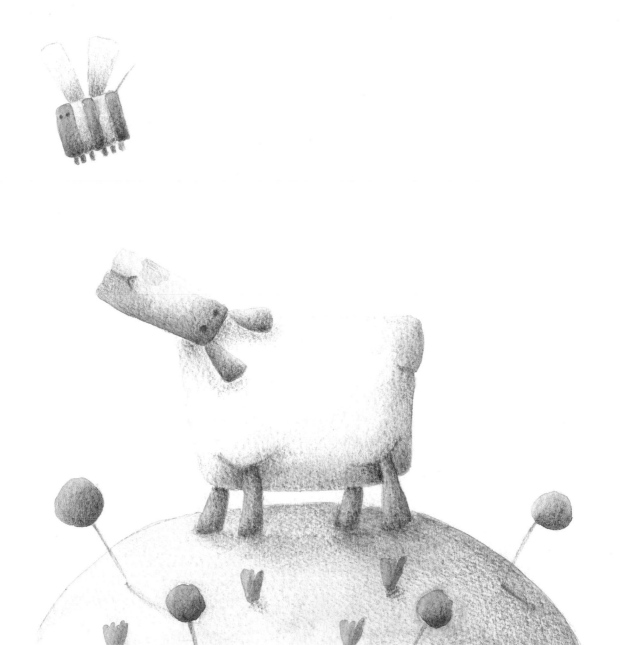

ane

The Shepherd had told of the danger outside,
but little sheep thought that he probably lied.
So slowly the little sheep went down the track,
and at the end of the lane he never looked back.

Orchard

The orchard had apples and pears on the trees and butterflies danced on the cool summer breeze.

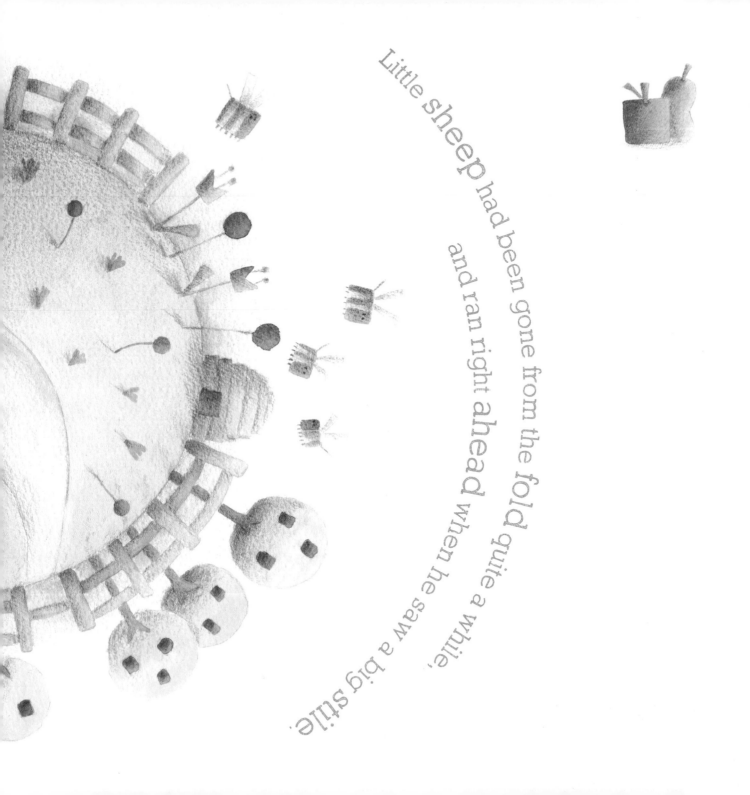

Little sheep had been gone from the fold quite a while,
and ran right ahead when he saw a big stile.

Over and
under he tried
to go through,
but something so
simple was quite
hard to do.

He finally got
through with
a **push** and a
squeeze,
and continued his
journey on into
the **trees.**

Stile

Little sheep went through the trees till he heard
a wolf start to howl, and he got very scared.

He should have **listened** to what Shepherd had said,
and **wished** he was back in the fold **safe** in bed.

rees

He tried to run home through the trees, but he found
he was lost and he fell in a hole in the ground.
He couldn't climb out, as the hole was too deep
for those with short legs like the lost little sheep.

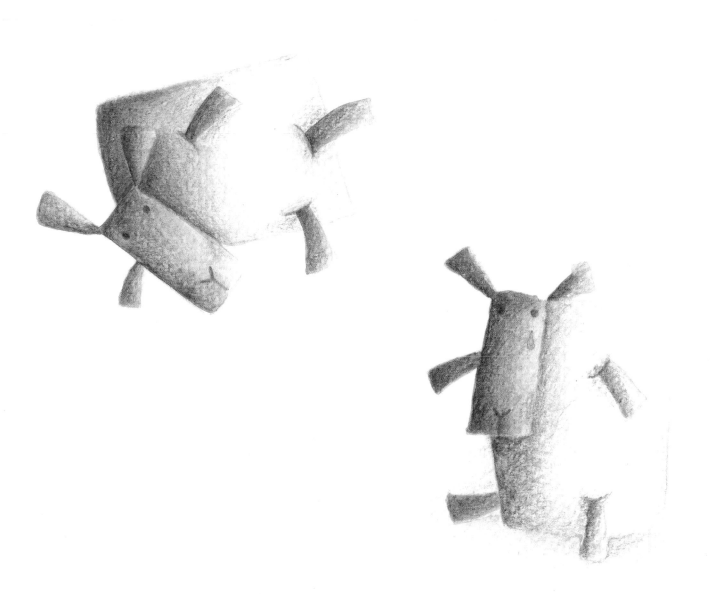

1 2 3 4 5 6 7 8... 95 96 97 98 99?

Back in the field Shepherd started to count,
100 sheep should have been the amount,
but counting to 99 Shepherd did see,
one less of his precious sheep than there should be.

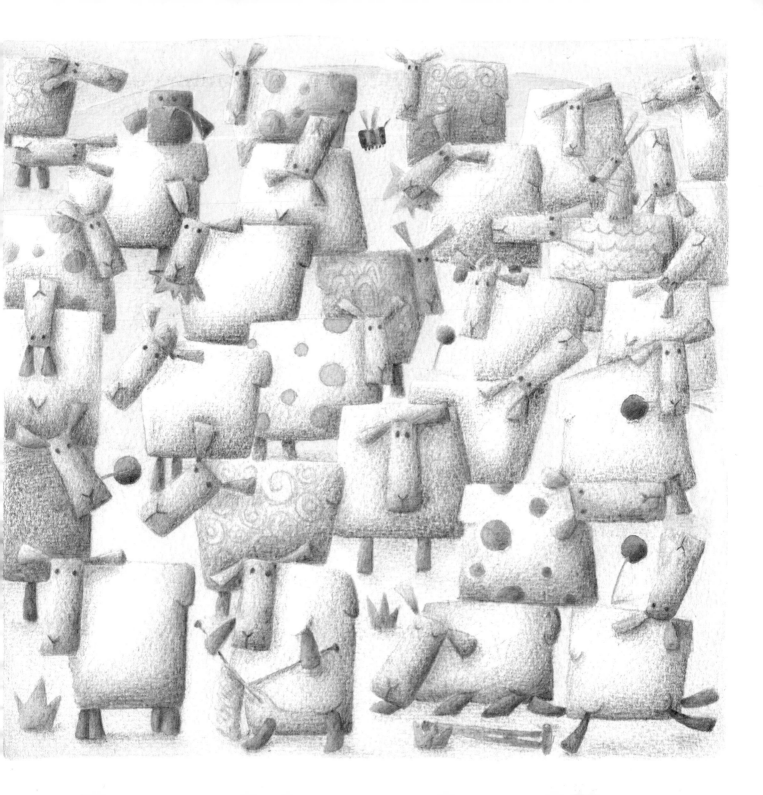

He started to count all the sheep once again,
the twins, little black one, the one that was lame.

Looking around he noticed the gate, and knew little sheep must have made an escape.

He started to search high and low on the lane,
hoping to find little sheep once again.
He went through the orchard and over the stile,
all the time looking for little sheep's smile.

Sheep was so scared what the Shepherd would say,
knowing the trouble he'd brought his own way.
But hearing the Shepherd calling for him,
a 'baaa' escaped that he couldn't keep in.

Shepherd was **happy** to see his **sheep** there,
and **helped** him right out with no time to **spare**.

Sheep was so tired he fell straight to sleep,

and dreamed of his field and the 99 sheep.

But wolf had missed out on catching his dinner,

and settled for fish and chips to stop getting thinner!

The little sheep had become lost

when he went his own way

and didn't stay where the Shepherd

had said it was safe.

Just like the little sheep in this story, we have all gone
our own way and strayed from the good Shepherd, God.
He doesn't want any of us to remain lost, and he loves
us so much that he sent his only son, Jesus, to find us.

Jesus went to the cross to take the punishment for the wrong things we have done, and if we trust in him, one day he will take us back with him to his fold, heaven.

In John chapter 10 verse 11 Jesus says: "I am the good Shepherd. The good Shepherd lays down his life for the sheep."

This story was first told by Jesus 2,000 years ago
but it has been retold many times by
Beach Team members over the last 60 years.

This version which uses the initials of
Lane, Orchard, Stile and Trees to spell LOST
was put together by a Beach Team leader many years
ago. Bethan has beautifully put it in verse form.

In fact Bethan and her husband James are involved in
Beach Teams – maybe you met them this year.

It will help you to stay close to Jesus if you read the Bible and go to a good church where they have a Sunday school or Bible club. The Postal Bible Club can help you understand the Bible. With PBC you will get a pack sent to you each month with Bible stories and quizzes. It's fun and it's **free**! You can even win prizes.

If you want any help to find a Sunday school or Bible club near to where you live, or if you want to sign up for the Postal Bible Club, please ask your mum or dad to contact The Beach Team with the following details:

Your name. Your address. Your date of birth.

Send the request to:

The Beach Team, Spring Cottage, Spring Road, Leeds, LS6 1AD

or office@thebeachteam.org

(The request must come from the parent or guardian.)

The Lost Sheep

Text and Illustrations © 2013. Bethan Lycett and Hannah Stout.

Published by 10Publishing, a division of 10ofThose Limited.

ISBN 9781909611078

Design and Typeset by: Diane Bainbridge.

Printed in the UK.

10Publishing, a division of 10ofthose.com

9D Centurion Court, Farington, Leyland, PR25 3UQ, England

Email: info@10ofthose.com

Website: www.10ofthose.com